WELCOME CHRISTMAS!
A Garland of Poems

Also by Anne Thaxter Eaton

THE ANIMALS' CHRISTMAS

READING WITH CHILDREN

TREASURE FOR THE TAKING

A ROUND DOZEN

DECORATED BY VALENTI ANGELO

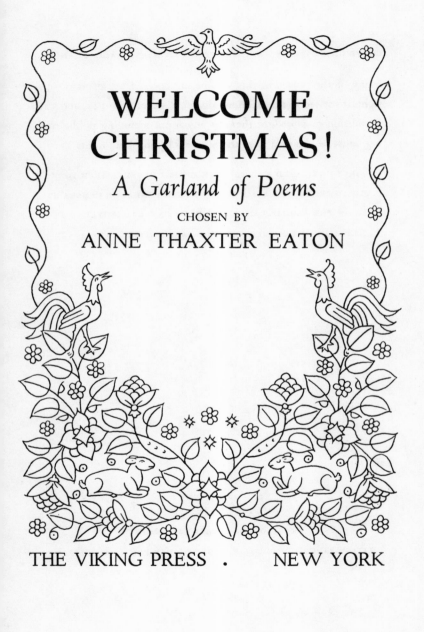

WELCOME CHRISTMAS!

A Garland of Poems

CHOSEN BY

ANNE THAXTER EATON

THE VIKING PRESS . NEW YORK

9   10   11   12   13   76   75   74   73   72
821.08   1. CHRISTMAS POETRY
LITHOGRAPHED IN THE U. S. A. BY MURRAY PRINTING COMPANY

Contents

Foreword

Ever since the angels sang to the wondering shepherds the first Christmas carol of peace on earth, good will to men, Christmas has been celebrated with song and verse.

Poets thinking of the starry sky, the woolly sheep and patient shepherds, the Three Kings riding from the East in jeweled, golden state to find in the shadowy stable the Mother and the Child, each year make new songs that deepen our sense of the holy, magical season. Each year we go back to reread the Christmas poems we loved as children, to feel again in the words of the carols the wonder which was and is so much a part of Christmas for us. Families sing together the carols, old and new; the lonely traveler hums the air and murmurs the words of his childhood's favorite Christmas song.

Welcome Christmas! brings together some of the old, well-known poems and carols, some of the new; but all, new or old, were chosen because they have in them the inner spirit of the season, because they suggest not only a happy but a blessed Christmas.

—ANNE THAXTER EATON

WELCOME
CHRISTMAS!
A Garland of Poems

Christmas Eve

In holly hedges starving birds
   Silently mourn the setting year;
Upright like silver-plated swords
   The flags stand in the frozen mere.

The mistletoe we still adore
   Upon the twisted hawthorn grows:
In antique gardens hellebore
   Puts forth its blushing Christmas rose.

Shrivell'd and purple, cheek by jowl,
   The hips and haws hang drearily;
Roll'd in a ball the sulky owl
   Creeps far into his hollow tree.

In abbeys and cathedrals dim
   The birth of Christ is acted o'er:
The Kings of Cologne worship him,
   Balthazar, Jasper, Melchior.

The shepherds in the field at night
   Beheld an angel glory-clad,
And shrank away with sore affright.
   "Be not afraid," the angel bade.

"I bring good news to king and clown,
   To you here crouching on the sward:
For there is born in David's town
   A Saviour which is Christ the Lord.

"Behold the babe is swathed, and laid
    Within a manger." Straight there stood
Beside the angel all arrayed
    A heavenly multitude.

"Glory to God," they sang; "and peace,
    Good pleasure among men."
The wondrous message of release!
    Glory to God again!

Hark! Hark! the waits, far up the street!
    A distant, ghostly charm unfolds,
Of magic music wild and sweet,
    Anomes and clarigolds.

—JOHN DAVIDSON

The Friendly Beasts

Jesus our brother, strong and good,
Was humbly born in a stable rude,
And the friendly beasts around Him stood,
Jesus our brother, strong and good.

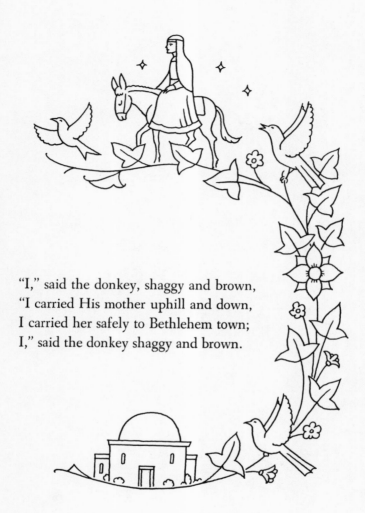

"I," said the donkey, shaggy and brown,
"I carried His mother uphill and down,
I carried her safely to Bethlehem town;
I," said the donkey shaggy and brown.

"I," said the cow, all white and red,
"I gave Him my manger for His bed,
I gave Him my hay to pillow His head,
I," said the cow all white and red.

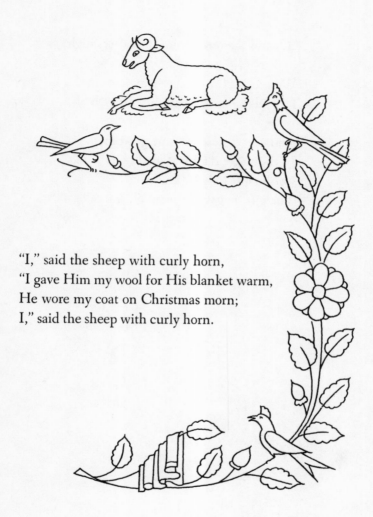

"I," said the sheep with curly horn,
"I gave Him my wool for His blanket warm,
He wore my coat on Christmas morn;
I," said the sheep with curly horn.

"I," said the dove, from the rafters high,
"Cooed Him to sleep, my mate and I;
We cooed Him to sleep, my mate and I;
I," said the dove, from the rafters high.

And every beast by some good spell,
In the stable dark was glad to tell,
Of the gift he gave Immanuel,
The gift he gave Immanuel.

(Twelfth-Century Carol)

The Oxen

Christmas Eve, and twelve of the clock,
  "Now they are all on their knees,"
An elder said as we sat in a flock
  By the embers in hearthside ease.

We pictured the meek mild creatures where
  They dwelt in their strawy pen,
Nor did it occur to one of us there
  To doubt they were kneeling then.

So fair a fancy few would weave
  In these years! Yet, I feel,
If someone said on Christmas Eve,
  "Come; see the oxen kneel,

"In the lonely barton by yonder coomb
  Our childhood used to know,"
I should go with him in the gloom,
  Hoping it might be so.

—THOMAS HARDY

Carol of the Birds

Whence comes this rush of wings afar,
Following straight the Noël star?
Birds from the woods in wondrous flight,
Bethlehem seek this Holy Night.

"Tell us, ye birds, why come ye here,
Into this stable, poor and drear?"
"Hast'ning we seek the new-born King,
And all our sweetest music bring."

Hark how the green-finch bears his part,
Philomel, too, with tender heart,
Chants from her leafy dark retreat,
Re, mi, fa, sol, in accents sweet.

Angels and shepherds, birds of the sky,
Come where the Son of God doth lie;
Christ on earth with man doth dwell,
Join in the shout, Noël, Noël.

—BAS-QUÉRCY

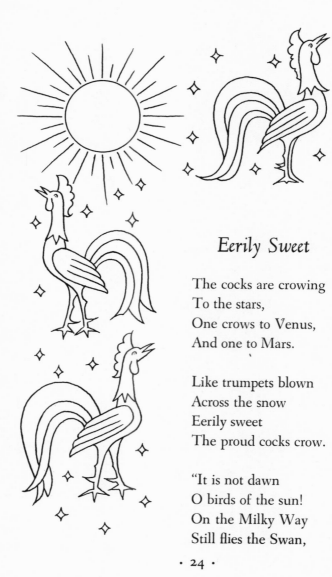

Eerily Sweet

The cocks are crowing
To the stars,
One crows to Venus,
And one to Mars.

Like trumpets blown
Across the snow
Eerily sweet
The proud cocks crow.

"It is not dawn
O birds of the sun!
On the Milky Way
Still flies the Swan,

"And great Orion
Strides through the air,
And Berenice
Lets down her hair.

"It is not dawn
O birds of the day!
Why do you crow
With the sun far away?"

The cocks crow loud
And the cocks crow clear,
Across the snow
'Tis a joy to hear.

"Once long ago
When the world was young
Over a manger
A bright star hung.

"Marvelled both man
And beast at the sight,
But the cocks saluted
The holy light.

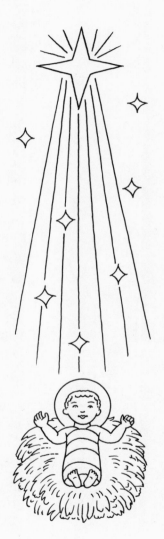

"Proudly they stood
And clapped their wings
To welcome the star
Of the King of kings!

"And now sometimes
Across the snow
We remember that night
And rise, and crow,

"And repeat the chant
To that star thrice blest—
'Christus, Christus
Natus est!' "

Like trumpets blown
Across the snow
Eerily sweet
The proud cocks crow.

—ELIZABETH COATSWORTH

Christated Is Born

Christus natus est, the Cock
Croweth to the lazy clock.
Christus natus est, he crows;
Christus—and the Raven knows,
And the Lambs, as you shall hear.
Loudly croweth Chanticleer,
With an eager, piercing sound,
To the Beasts that lie around;
And they question and reply,
While the Sun mounts up the sky.
Quando? Quando? and again—
That's the Duck who's asking *when?*
In hac nocte, the Raven croaks
From the old snow-laden oaks.
Quando? Quando? from beyond
The willows by the frozen pond.
In hac nocte, croaks the Raven
From its bare winter's haven.
Ubi? Ubi? the Bull lows,
Standing black against the snows;
And the Lambs: *In Bethlehem:*
It was God who told it them.

—JOHN ALEXANDER CHAPMAN

I Saw a Stable

I saw a stable, low and very bare,
A little child in a manger.
The oxen knew Him, had Him in their care,
To men He was a stranger.
The safety of the world was lying there,
And the world's danger.

—MARY ELIZABETH COLERIDGE

Carol

In the bleak mid-winter
 Frosty wind made moan,
Earth stood hard as iron,
 Water like a stone:
Snow had fallen, snow on snow,
 Snow on snow,
In the bleak mid-winter,
 Long ago.

Our God, heaven cannot hold Him
  Nor earth sustain;
Heaven and earth shall flee away
  When He comes to reign:
In the bleak mid-winter
  A stable place sufficed
The Lord God Almighty,
  Jesus Christ.

Enough for Him, whom Cherubim
  Worship night and day,
A breastful of milk
  And a manger full of hay;
Enough for Him, whom angels
  Fall down before,
The ox and ass and camel
  Which adore.

Angels and Archangels
  May have gathered there,
Cherubim and Seraphim
  Thronged the air—
But only His mother
  In her maiden bliss
Worshipped the Belovèd
  With a kiss.

What can I give Him
  Poor as I am?
If I were a shepherd
  I would bring a lamb;
If I were a wise man
  I would do my part—
Yet what can I give Him,
  Give my heart.

—CHRISTINA ROSSETTI

Earth and Sky

(They talk to each other on Christmas Eve)

Earth:	Oh Sky, you look so drear!
Sky:	Oh Earth, you look so bare!
Earth:	How chilly you appear!
Sky:	How empty you lie there!
Sky:	My winds blow icy cold.
Earth:	My flowers have gone from me.
Sky:	Yet I've one Star of gold.
Earth:	And I have one green Tree.
Sky:	I'll set my Star on high
	Alone in its own light
	For any Child to spy
	Who wakes on Christmas Night.

Earth:	I'll hang my Tree with toys,
	Like fruit and flowers gay,
	For little girls and boys
	To pick on Christmas Day.

They say	Then let the soft snow fall,
together:	And let the cold wind blow!
	We have in spite of all
	A pretty thing to show;

Yes, Christmas Eve and Morn
We'll show our pretty thing
To every baby born
Of Beggar-man or King.

Earth:	Oh Sky, you look so clear!
Sky:	Oh Earth, you look so fair!
Earth:	How bright your Star shines here.
Sky:	How green your Tree grows there.

—ELEANOR FARJEON

The Christmas Tree

The holly's up, the house is all bright,
The tree is ready, the candles alight:
Rejoice and be glad, all children tonight!

The mother sings of our Lord's good grace
Whereby the Child who saved our race
Was born and adored in a lowly place.

Once more the shepherds, as she sings,
Bend low, and angels touch their strings:
With "Glory" they hail the King of kings.

The children listening round the tree
Can hear the heavenly minstrelsy,
The manger's marvel they can see.

Let every house be ready tonight—
The children gathered, the candles alight—
That music to hear, to see that sight.

—CARL AUGUST PETER CORNELIUS
Translated by H. N. Bate

Nowel

Holly dark: pale Mistletoe—
Christmas Eve is come, and lo,
Wild are the bells across the snow,
Waits in the dark streets carolling go;
   "Nowel! Nowel!" they shout—and, oh,
     How live out the day!
Each breath I breathe turns to a sigh;
     My heart is flown away;
The things I see around me seem
Entranced with light—as in a dream;
The candles dazzle in my eyes,
And every leaping fireflame tries
     To sing, what none could say.

—WALTER DE LA MARE

How far is it to Bethlehem?

How far is it to Bethlehem?
   Not very far.
Shall we find the stable-room
   Lit by a star?

Can we see the little Child?
   Is He within?
If we lift the wooden latch,
   May we go in?

May we stroke the creatures there—.
   Ox, ass, or sheep?
May we peep like them and see
   Jesus asleep?

If we touch His tiny hand,
  Will He awake?
Will He know we've come so far
  Just for His sake?

Great kings have precious gifts,
  And we have naught;
Little smiles and little tears
  Are all we brought.

For all weary children
   Mary must weep;
Here, on His bed of straw,
   Sleep, children, sleep.

God, in His mother's arms,
   Babes in the byre,
Sleep, as they sleep who find
   Their heart's desire.

—FRANCES CHESTERTON

Cradle Hymn

Away in a manger, no crib for a bed,
The little Lord Jesus laid down his sweet head.
The stars in the bright sky looked down where he lay—
The little Lord Jesus asleep on the hay.

The cattle are lowing, the baby awakes,
But little Lord Jesus, no crying he makes.
I love thee, Lord Jesus! Look down from the sky,
And stay by my cradle till morning is nigh.

—MARTIN LUTHER

By the Crib

The small child-angels
New 'scaped from Heaven,
Like a flock of rose-leaves
On snow new driven.

They came hurrying, winging
To the stable-stall,
Like a bush of roses
On a June wall.

They perched by the manger
In rafter and roof,
For their wings the stable
Was weather proof.

There were kings and shepherds
And the sheep-dog came,
The ass and oxen
And a new-born lamb.

Lions and tigers
Knelt in the door,
Their wrath forgotten
And their warfare o'er.

The wren and robin
Came hopping in;
And the snake came wriggling
With his spotted skin.

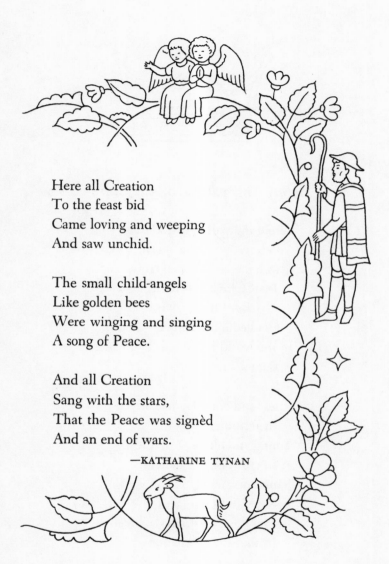

Here all Creation
To the feast bid
Came loving and weeping
And saw unchid.

The small child-angels
Like golden bees
Were winging and singing
A song of Peace.

And all Creation
Sang with the stars,
That the Peace was signèd
And an end of wars.

—KATHARINE TYNAN

Before the paling of the stars

Before the paling of the stars,
  Before the winter morn,
Before the earliest cockcrow,
  Jesus Christ was born:
    Born in a stable,
  Cradled in a manger,
In the world His hands had made
  Born a stranger.

Priest and King lay fast asleep
  In Jerusalem,
Young and old lay fast asleep
  In crowded Bethlehem:
Saint and Angel, ox and ass,
  Kept a watch together
Before the Christmas daybreak
  In the winter weather.

Jesus on His Mother's breast
　　In the stable cold,
Spotless Lamb of God was He,
　　Shepherd of the fold:
Let us kneel with Mary Maid,
　　With Joseph bent and hoary,
With Saint and Angel, ox and ass,
　　To hail the King of Glory.

—CHRISTINA ROSSETTI

Christmas Eve in Ireland

Not a cabin in the Glen shuts its door tonight,
    Lest the travellers abroad knock in vain and pass,
Just a humble gentleman and a lady bright
    And she to be riding on an ass.

Grief is on her goodman, that the inns deny
    Shelter to his dearest Dear in her hour of need;
That her Babe of royal birth, starriest, most high,
    Has not where to lay His head.

Must they turn in sadness to the cattle byre
    And the kind beasts once again shake the bed for Him?
Not a cabin in the Glen but heaps wood on the fire
    And keeps its lamps a-trim.

Now the woman makes the bed, smoothes the linen sheet,
    Spreads the blanket soft and white, that her own hands
        spun,
Whisht! Is that the ass that comes, on his four little feet,
    Carrying the Holy One?

Nay, 'twas but the wind and rain, the sand on the floor.
　　A bitter night, yea, cruel, for folk to be abroad.
And she, not fit for hardship, outside a fast-closed door,
　　And her Son the Son of God!

Is it the moon that's turning the dark world to bright?
　　Is it some wonderful dawning in the night and cold?
Whisht! Did you see a shining One and Him to be clad in
　　　light
　　And the wings and head of Him gold?

Who are then these people, hurrying, hasting, those,
　　And they all looking up in the sky this night of wondrous
　　　things?
Oh, those I think be shepherdmen, and they that follow
　　close,
　　I think, by their look, be kings.

Not a cabin in the Glen shuts the door till day,
　　Lest the heavenly travellers come, knock again in vain.
All night the dulcimers, flutes and hautboys play,
　　And the angels walk with men.

—KATHARINE TYNAN

Bethlehem

A little child,
   A shining star,
A stable rude,
   The door ajar.

Yet in that place,
   So crude, forlorn,
The Hope of all
   The world was born.
           (Author unknown)

The Barn

"I am tired of this barn!" said the colt,
"And every day it snows.
Outside there's no grass any more
And icicles grow on my nose.
I am tired of hearing the cows
Breathing and talking together.
I am sick of these clucking hens.
I *hate* stables and winter weather!"

"Hush, little colt," said the mare,
"And a story I will tell
Of a barn like this one of ours
And the wonders that there befell.
It was weather much like this
And the beasts stood as we stand now
In the warm good dark of the barn—
A horse and an ass and a cow."

"And sheep?" asked the colt. "Yes, sheep
And a pig and a goat and a hen.
All of the beasts of the barnyard
The usual servants of men.
And into their midst came a lady
And she was as cold as death,
But the animals leaned above her
And made her warm with their breath.

"There was her baby born
And laid to sleep in the hay
While music flooded the rafters
And the barn was as light as day,
And angels and kings and shepherds
Came to worship the Babe from afar,
But we looked at Him first of all creatures
By the bright strange light of a star!"

—ELIZABETH COATSWORTH

The Ox and the Ass

"What do you see in the sky, brown Ox,
Gazing so far, so far?"
"I can remember when such a night
Was lit by a wondrous star!"

"Why are you twitching your ears, grey Ass,
Listening so long, so long?"
"Once, earth was filled with the rush of wings
And my ears with a joyful song!"

"Why are you sniffing the air, brown Ox,
So eager and so intent?"
"I can remember when kingly forms
Brought gifts with a strange sweet scent."

"Why do you muzzle the hay, grey Ass,
With touch so light, so light?"
"There was a Child whose bed was hay
On such a starlit night!"

—EDITH SIMPSON

"While Shepherds Watched Their Flocks by Night"

Like small curled feathers, white and soft,
    The little clouds went by,
Across the moon, and past the stars,
    And down the western sky:
In upland pastures, where the grass
    With frosted dew was white,
Like snowy clouds the young sheep lay,
    That first. best Christmas night.

The shepherds slept; and, glimmering faint,
    With twist of thin, blue smoke,
Only their fire's crackling flames
    The tender silence broke—
Save when a young lamb raised his head,
    Or, when the night wind blew,
A nesting bird would softly stir,
    Where dusky olives grew—

With finger on her solemn lip,
    Night hushed the shadowy earth,
And only stars and angels saw
    The little Saviour's birth;
Then came such a flash of silver light
    Across the bending skies,
The wondering shepherds woke, and hid
    Their frightened, dazzled eyes!

And all their gentle sleepy flock
   Looked up, then slept again,
Nor knew the light that dimmed the stars
   Brought endless Peace to men—
Nor even heard the gracious words
   That down the ages ring—
"The Christ is born! the Lord has come,
   Good-will on earth to bring!"

Then o'er the moonlit, misty fields,
   Dumb with the world's great joy,
The shepherds sought the white-walled town,
   Where lay the baby boy—
And oh, the gladness of the world,
   The glory of the skies,
Because the longed-for Christ looked up
   In Mary's happy eyes!

—MARGARET DELAND

Shepherds' Carol

At Christmas, firstling lambs are dropped,
And all night long, in the frosty fold
We cosset the lambs, and tend the ewes,
And thatch the wattles against the cold.

In the still night the owls are calling,
One by one the lights have gone,
And only that in the church is burning,
And quiet as snow the worshippers come.

The stars are shining, as sharp and as cold
As the ice in the brook, as the frost on the fern,
And, as we work, we remember the old
Tale we were told, of those of our trade.

Who, tending their sheep, as we, long ago
On a hilltop lay, with the village below,
And one by one, torches and fires
Died out, and only the lamp-soft glow

Burned in a stable, and burned in a star,
And in the eyes and the flaming hair
Of Two who came, bright as love, white as fear,
And told that the Shepherd of men was born.

Shepherd and Lamb in one, they say,
So fitting it is, we think, on His day
The ewe should labour, the lamb be born,
And shepherds watch, and listen, and pray.

—MARGARET STANLEY-WRENCH

The Shepherd's Tale

A strange night it was,
With the air icy and still
And the sheep huddled together
Against the cold hill.
I took my strongest staff
And, striding into the night,
Followed, as one that dreamed,
A great star's light.
And so to Bethlehem's inn

I came, as the cocks crowed,
And my tired feet flagged
On the frosty road.
Over the stable roof
The star shone bright,
Drawing me to the door
With a beckoning light.
Only a man was there
With his wife, and Babe new-born,
Sharing the oxen's straw
In the bitter dawn;
Only a homeless maid
With her Babe at breast,
Yet I knew when she smiled on me
That I was blessed;
And I strode home with the pride
Of one who has met with Kings,
While the air trembled with song
And the beating of wings.

—EDITH SIMPSON

Woods' Litany

Now birds that sleep in brittle trees,
Sparrows and jays and chickadees,
The last, last robin and the crow,
Awake beneath your thatch of snow
And hearing bells of midnight ring
Rouse up and through the darkness sing
How in your dreams across the snows,
A star, bright as a sun, arose.

And all you creatures furred and wise
That in the darkness close bright eyes,
Twitch quivering nostrils, leave your sleep
And from your dens and hollows creep.
See how the deer among the thorns
Raises the crosses of his horns,
While like soft candles at a feast
The doe's eyes turn to face the east!

Gentle is he
As windless snow.
Kind as a tree
With shelter below.

As a stream of water
In August heat,
As a blueberry bush
Hidden and sweet,

Such is he
Who is born this day
In Bethlehem
So far away!

—ELIZABETH COATSWORTH

Christmas Eve Legend

The woods were still and the snow was deep,
But there was no creature who could sleep.

The fox and the vixen ran together
Silently through the starry weather.

The buck and the doe and the fawn came drifting
Into the clearing. The rabbit, lifting

His ears, shook white from the twigs he brushed;
The chattering squirrel for once was hushed

As he sat with his paws against his breast,
And the bobcat crouched on the mountain crest.

Safe in the fold the silver sheep
Told the young lambs not to leap.

In the shadowy stable the horses stood
Hearing the quietness in the wood,

And the cattle sighed in the fragrant barn,
Waiting the instant of the morn.

The stars stood at midnight, and tame or wild,
All creatures knelt to worship the Child.

—FRANCES FROST

Carol

Outlanders, whence come ye last?
The snow in the street and the wind on the door,
Through what green seas and great have ye past?
Minstrels and maids, stand forth on the floor.

From far away we come to you,
The snow in the street and the wind on the door,
To tell of great tidings strange and true,
Minstrels and maids, stand forth on the floor.

For as we wandered far and wide,
The snow in the street and the wind on the door,
What hap do you deem there should us betide!
Minstrels and maids, stand forth on the floor.

Under a bent when the night was deep,
The snow in the street and the wind on the door,
There lay three shepherds tending their sheep:
Minstrels and maids, stand forth on the floor.

"O ye shepherds, what have ye seen,
  The snow in the street and the wind on the door,
To slay your sorrow, and heal your teen?"
  Minstrels and maids, stand forth on the floor.

"In an ox-stall this night we saw,
  The snow in the street and the wind on the door,
A babe and a maid without a flaw:
  Minstrels and maids, stand forth on the floor.

"And a marvellous song we straight did hear,
  The snow in the street and the wind on the door,
That slew our sorrow and healed our care."
  Minstrels and maids, stand forth on the floor.

News of a fair and a marvellous thing,
  The snow in the street and the wind on the door,
Nowell, nowell, nowell, we sing!
  Minstrels and maids, stand forth on the floor.

—WILLIAM MORRIS

Shepherds, in the field abiding

Shepherds, in the field abiding,
    Tell us, when the Seraph bright
Greeted you with wondrous tiding,
    What ye saw and heard that night.
        Gloria in excelsis Deo.

We beheld (it is no fable)
    God incarnate, King of bliss,
Swathed and cradled in a stable,
    And the angel strain was this:
        Gloria in excelsis Deo.

Quiristers on high were singing
   Jesus and his Virgin-birth;
Heav'nly bells the while a-ringing
   "Peace, goodwill to men on earth."
     Gloria in excelsis Deo.

Thanks, good herdmen; true your story;
   Have with you to Bethlehem:
Angels hymn the King of Glory:
   Carol we with you and them.
     Gloria in excelsis Deo.
        —GEORGE RATCLIFFE WOODWARD

Carol

When the herds were watching
In the midnight chill,
Came a spotless lambkin
From the heavenly hill.

Snow was on the mountains,
And the wind was cold,
When from God's own garden
Dropped a rose of gold.

When 'twas bitter winter,
Houseless and forlorn
In a star-lit stable
Christ the Babe was born.

Welcome, heavenly lambkin;
Welcome, golden Rose;
Alleluia, Baby
In the swaddling clothes!

—WILLIAM CANTON

Before Dawn

Dim-berried is the mistletoe
With globes of sheenless grey;
The holly 'mid ten thousand thorns
Smoulders its fires away;
And in the manger Jesu sleeps
      This Christmas Day.

Bull unto bull with hollow throat
Makes echo every hill,
Cold sheep in pastures thick with snow
The air with bleatings fill;
While of His mother's heart this Babe
      Takes His sweet will.

All flowers and butterflies lie hid,
The blackbird and the thrush
Pipe but a little as they flit
Restless from bush to bush;
Even to the robin Gabriel hath
    Cried softly, "Hush!"

Now night is astir with burning stars
In darkness of the snow;
Burdened with frankincense and myrrh
And gold the Strangers go
Into a dusk where one dim lamp
    Burns faintly, Lo!

No snowdrop yet its small head nods,
In winds of winter drear;
No lark at casement in the sky
Sings matins shrill and clear;
Yet in this frozen mirk the Dawn
    Breathes, Spring is here!

—WALTER DE LA MARE

I heard a bird sing

I heard a bird sing
In the dark of December.
A magical thing
And sweet to remember.

"We are nearer to Spring
Than we were in September,"
I heard a bird sing
In the dark of December.

—OLIVER HERFORD

A Christmas Carol

The Christ-child lay on Mary's lap,
His hair was like a light.
(O weary, weary were the world,
But here is all aright.)

The Christ-child lay on Mary's breast,
His hair was like a star.
(O stern and cunning are the Kings,
But here the true hearts are.)

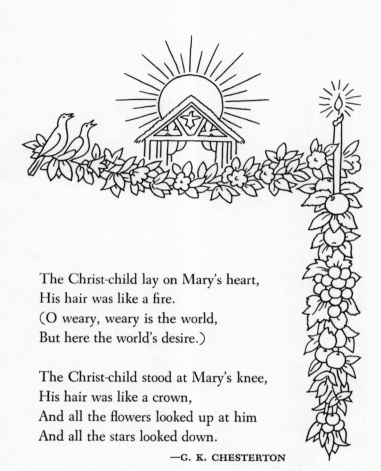

The Christ-child lay on Mary's heart,
His hair was like a fire.
(O weary, weary is the world,
But here the world's desire.)

The Christ-child stood at Mary's knee,
His hair was like a crown,
And all the flowers looked up at him
And all the stars looked down.

—G. K. CHESTERTON

Christmas at Freelands

A snowy field! A stable piled
With straw! A donkey's sleepy pow!
A mother beaming on a child!
A manger, and a munching cow!
—These we all remember now—
And airy voices, heard afar!
And three Magicians, and a Star!

Two thousand times of snow declare
That on the Christmas of the year
There is a singing in the air;
And all who listen for it hear
A fairy chime, a seraph strain,
Telling He is born again,
—That all we love is born again.

—JAMES STEPHENS

Ox and Donkey's Carol

The Christ-child lay in the ox's stall,
The stars shone great and the stars shone small,
But one bright star outshone them all.

The cattle stood in the cleanly straw
And strange to them was the sight they saw.
The ox and the donkey watched with awe.

The shepherds ran from the uplands wide,
The sheepbells tinkled, the angels cried
Joy to the dreaming countryside.

The three kings bowed at the stable door,
Their raiment trailed on the dusty floor.
They saw the light they had journeyed for.

The kings came last in a lordly throng,
The shepherds ran in the space of a song,
But the beasts had been there all night long.
      Noël Noël Noël!

—SISTER MARIS STELLA

Carol

Villagers all, this frosty tide,
Let your doors swing open wide,
Though wind may follow, and snow beside,
Yet draw us in by your fire to bide;
   Joy shall be yours in the morning!

Here we stand in the cold and the sleet,
Blowing fingers and stamping feet,
Come from far away you to greet—
You by the fire and we in the street—
  Bidding you joy in the morning!

For ere one half of the night was gone,
Sudden a star has led us on,
Raining bliss and benison—
Bliss tomorrow and more anon,
  Joy for every morning!

Goodman Joseph toiled through the snow—
Saw the star o'er a stable low;
Mary she might not further go—
Welcome thatch, and litter below!
   Joy was hers in the morning!

And then they heard the angels tell,
"Who were the first to cry Nowell?
Animals all, as it befell,
In the stable where they did dwell!
   Joy shall be theirs in the morning!"

—KENNETH GRAHAME

Song

Neither in halls, nor yet in bowers
Born would He not be.
Neither in castles, nor yet in towers,
That seemly were to see,
But at His Father's will,
Betwixt an ox and ass,
Jesu born He was;
Heaven He bring us till!

(*From an* Old Nativity Play)

Sunny Bank, or, I Saw Three Ships

As I sat on a sunny bank,
On Christmas Day in the morning,

I spied three ships come sailing by,
On Christmas Day in the morning.

And who should be with those three ships
But Joseph and his fair lady!

O he did whistle and she did sing,
On Christmas Day in the morning.

And all the bells on earth did ring,
On Christmas Day in the morning.

For joy that our Saviour he was born
On Christmas Day in the morning.

(Old Broadside)

Words from an Old Spanish Carol

Shall I tell you who will come
    to Bethlehem on Christmas Morn,
Who will kneel them gently down
    before the Lord, new-born?

One small fish from the river,
    with scales of red, red gold,
One wild bee from the heather,
    one gray lamb from the fold,
One ox from the high pasture,
    one black bull from the herd,
One goatling from the far hills,
    one white, white bird.

And many children—God give them grace,
bringing tall candles to light Mary's face.

Shall I tell you who will come
    to Bethlehem on Christmas Morn,
Who will kneel them gently down
    before the Lord, new-born?

—RUTH SAWYER

Christmas Day

Last night in the open shippen
   The infant Jesus lay,
While cows stood at the hay-crib
   Twitching the sweet hay.

As I trudged through the snow-fields
   That lay in their own light,
A thorn-bush with its shadow
   Stood doubled on the night.

And I stayed on my journey
   To listen to the cheep
Of a small bird in the thorn-bush
   I woke from its puffed sleep.

The bright stars were my angels
   And with the heavenly host
I sang praise to the Father,
   The Son and Holy Ghost.

—ANDREW YOUNG

Carol

The Ox said to the Ass, said he, all on a Christmas night:
"Do you hear the pipe of the shepherds a-whistling over the
    hill?
That is the angels' music they play for their delight,
 Glory to God in the highest and peace upon earth, good
    will' . . .
Nowell, nowell, my masters, God lieth low in stall,
And the poor labouring Ox was here before you all."

The Ass said to the Ox, said he, all on a Christmas day:
"Do you hear the golden bridles come clinking out of the
    east?
Those are the three wise Mages that ride from far away
To Bethlehem in Jewry to have their lore increased . . .
Nowell, nowell, my masters, God lieth low in stall,
And the poor foolish Ass was here before you all."

—**DOROTHY SAYERS**

· 86 ·

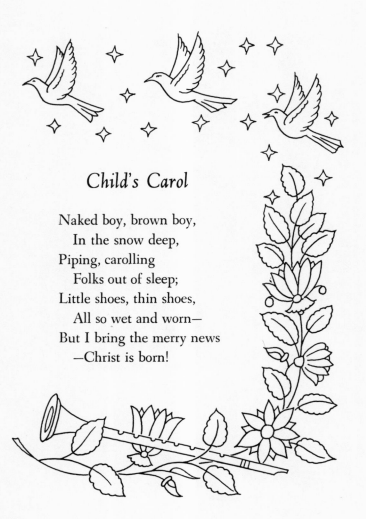

Child's Carol

Naked boy, brown boy,
　　In the snow deep,
Piping, carolling
　　Folks out of sleep;
Little shoes, thin shoes,
　　All so wet and worn—
But I bring the merry news
　　—Christ is born!

Rise, pretty mistress!
  Don a gay silk;
Give me for my good news
  Bread and new milk.
Joy, joy in Jewry,
  This very morn!
Far and far I carry it
  —Christ is born!

Back, back in Bethl'em,
  By the moon still,
There I saw a shepherd
  Sitting on a hill;
"Boy," said he, "bonny boy,
  Take you this horn,
Wend you now and wind it
  —Christ is born!"

And whenever people
　　Hear the merry blast,
Bells in every steeple,
　　Flags on every mast,
Holy boughs and holly
　　Adore and adorn,
Far and far and jubilant
　　—Christ is born!

Therefore I would have you
   People comprehend
Christ is born in Bethl'em
   For to be your friend:
For to bear the agony,
   For to wear the thorn,
For to die on Calvary
   —Christ is born.
   —ARTHUR QUILLER-COUCH

Ballad of the Epiphany

When Christ was born in Bethlehem,
Pan left his Sussex Downs,
To see three kings go riding by,
All in their robes and crowns;
And as they went in royal state,
Pan followed them, unseen,
Though tiny tufts of grass and flowers
Showed where his feet had been.

And when to Bethlehem they came,
Birds sang in every tree,
And Mary in the stable sat,
With Jesus on her knee;
And while the oxen munched their hay,
The kings with one accord
Placed gold and frankincense and myrrh
Before their infant Lord.

And when Pan peeped upon the scene,
The Christ Child clapped His hands,
And chuckled with delight to see
The god of pasture lands;
And Mary sang, "Magnificat"
Above the kneeling kings,
And angels circled overhead
On rainbow-coloured wings.

And many a little singing bird
Flew past the open door
To hop and chirrup in the straw
Above the stable floor;
Wrens, robins, linnets, goldfinches,
And many another one,
Flew in to show good fellowship
With Mary's newborn Son.

Then Pan stood up and played his pipes
Beside the manger-bed,
And every little bird went near
And raised its faithful head;
And one, most beautiful to see,
A fair and milk-white dove,
Arose and hovered in the air
To testify its love,

But when the kings looked up to find
Who made the piping sound,
They only saw white lilies shine,
Fresh-gathered, on the ground,
And through the doorway, and beyond,
A shaggy wild goat leap;
And in its gentle mother's arm,
The Baby fast asleep.

—CHARLES DALMON

Gates and Doors

There was a gentle hostler,
(And blessèd be his name!)
He opened up the stable
The night Our Lady came.
Our Lady and Saint Joseph,
He gave them food and bed.
And Jesus Christ has given him
A glory round his head.

So let the gate swing open
However poor the yard,
Lest weary people visit you
And find their passage barred;
Unlatch the door at midnight˙
And let your lantern's glow
Shine out to guide the traveller's feet
To you across the snow.

There was a courteous hostler,
(He is in Heaven tonight!)
He held Our Lady's bridle
And helped her to alight;
He spread clean straw before her
Whereon she might lie down,
And Jesus Christ has given him
An everlasting crown.

Unlock the door this evening,
And let your gate swing wide,
Let all who ask for shelter
Come speedily inside.
What if your yard be narrow?
What if your house be small?
There is a Guest is coming
Will glorify it all.

There was a joyous hostler
Who knelt on Christmas morn
Beside the radiant manger
Wherein his Lord was born.
His heart was full of laughter
His soul was full of bliss
When Jesus, on His Mother's lap
Gave him His hand to kiss.

Unbar your heart this evening
And keep no stranger out.
Take from your soul's great portal
The barrier of doubt.
To humble folk and weary
Give hearty welcoming,
Your breast shall be tomorrow
The cradle of a King.

—JOYCE KILMER

If ye would hear

If ye would hear the angels sing
   "Peace on earth and mercy mild,"
    Think of him who was once a child,
On Christmas Day in the morning.

If ye would hear the angels sing,
   Rise, and spread your Christmas fare;
    'Tis merrier still the more that share,
On Christmas Day in the morning.

Rise and bake your Christmas bread:
    Christians, rise! the world is bare,
    And blank, and dark with want and care,
Yet Christmas comes in the morning.

If ye would hear the angels sing,
    Rise, and light your Christmas fire:
    And see that ye pile the logs still higher
On Christmas Day in the morning.

Rise, and light your Christmas fire;
    Christians, rise! the world is old,
    And Time is weary, and worn, and cold,
Yet Christmas comes in the morning.

If ye would hear the angels sing,
    Christians! see ye let each door
    Stand wider than it e'er stood before,
On Christmas Day in the morning.

Rise, and open wide the door;
    Christians, rise! the world is wide,
    And many there be that stand outside,
Yet Christmas comes in the morning.

—DORA GREENWELL

The House of Christmas

There fared a mother driven forth
    Out of an inn to roam;
In the place where she was homeless
    All men are at home.
The crazy stable close at hand,
With shaking timber and shifting sand,
Grew a stronger thing to abide and stand
    Than the square stones of Rome.

For men are homesick in their homes,
    And strangers under the sun,
And they lay their heads in a foreign land
    Whenever the day is done.
Here we have battle and blazing eyes,
And chance and honour and high surprise;
But our homes are under miraculous skies
    Where the Yule tale was begun.

A child in a foul stable,
    Where the beasts feed and foam;
Only where He was homeless
    Are you and I at home;
We have hands that fashion and heads that know,
But our hearts we lost—how long ago!—
In a place no chart nor ship can show
    Under the sky's dome.

This world is wild as an old wives' tale,
    And strange the plain things are,
The earth is enough and the air is enough
    For our wonder and our war;
But our rest is as far as the fire-drake swings,
And our peace is put in impossible things
Where clashed and thundered unthinkable wings
    Round an incredible star.

To an open house in the evening
    Home shall men come,
To an older place than Eden
    And a taller town than Rome;
To the end of the way of the wandering star,
To the things that cannot be and that are,
To the place where God was homeless
    And all men are at home.

—G. K. CHESTERTON

Carol

High o'er the lonely hills
　　Black turns to grey,
Birdsong the valley fills,
　　Mists fold away;
Grey wakes to green again,
Beauty is seen again—
Gold and serene again
　　Dawneth the day.

So o'er the hills of life,
　　Stormy, forlorn,
Out of the cloud and strife
　　Sunrise is born;
Swift grows the light for us;
Ended is night for us;
Soundless and bright for us
　　Breaketh God's morn.

Hear we no beat of drums,
  Fanfare nor cry,
When Christ the herald comes
  Quietly nigh;
Splendour he makes on earth;
Colour awakes on earth;
Suddenly breaks on earth
  Light from the sky.

Bid then farewell to sleep:
  Rise up and run!
What though the hill be steep?
  Strength's in the sun.
Now shall you find at last
Night's left behind at last,
And for mankind at last
  Day has begun!

—JAN STRUTHER

Masters in this Hall

Masters in this Hall,
   Hear ye news today
Brought from over-sea,
   And ever I you pray:

Nowell! Nowell! Nowell!
Nowell sing we clear!
Holpen are all folk on earth,
Born is God's son so dear:
Nowell! Nowell! Nowell!
Nowell sing we loud!
God today hath poor folk raised
And cast a-down the proud.

Going o'er the hills,
   Through the milk-white snow,
Heard I ewes bleat
   While the wind did blow:

Shepherds many an one
   Sat among the sheep,
No man spake more word
   Than they had been asleep:

Quoth I, " Fellows mine,
    Why this guise sit ye?
Making but dull cheer,
    Shepherds though ye be?

"Shepherds should of right
    Leap and dance and sing,
Thus to see ye sit,
    Is a right strange thing":

Quoth these fellows then,
    "To Bethlem town we go,
To see a mighty lord
    Lie in manger low":

"How name ye this lord,
    Shepherds?" then said I,
"Very God," they said,
    "Come from Heaven high":

Then to Bethlem town
    We went two and two,
And in a sorry place
    Heard the oxen low:

Therein did we see
  A sweet and goodly may
And a fair old man;
  Upon the straw she lay:

And a little child
  On her arm had she,
"Wot ye who this is?"
  Said the hinds to me:

Ox and ass him know,
  Kneeling on their knee,
Wondrous joy had I
  This little babe to see:

This is Christ the Lord,
  Masters be ye glad!
Christmas is come in,
  And no folk should be sad.

—WILLIAM MORRIS

O'er the hill and o'er the vale

O'er the hill and o'er the vale
   Come three kings together,
Caring nought for snow and hail,
   Cold and wind and weather:
Now on Persia's sandy plains,
Now where Tigris swells with rains,
   They their camels tether;
Now through Syrian lands they go,
Now through Moab, faint and slow,
   Now o'er Edom's heather.

O'er the hill and o'er the vale,
　　Each king bears a present:
Wise men go a Child to hail,
　　Monarchs seek a Peasant:
And a star in front proceeds,
Over rocks and rivers leads,
　　Shines with beams incessant;
Therefore onward, onward still!
Ford the stream and climb the hill:
　　Love makes all things pleasant.

He is God ye go to meet:
  Therefore incense proffer:
He is King ye go to greet;
  Gold is in your coffer:
Also Man, He comes to share
Ev'ry woe that man can bear—
  Tempter, Railer, Scoffer:
Therefore now, against the day,
In the grave when Him they lay
  Myrrh ye also offer.

—J. M. NEALE

Bethlehem-Juda, 'twas there on a morn

Bethlehem-Juda, 'twas there on a morn
That Christ, in the days of King Herod, was born:
When from the East Country, o'er fell, frith and fen,
There came to Hierusalem certain Wise Men.

Saying, "We pray you, sirs, tell us the place,
Wherein he is born, who is King of your race.
For from the East Country we, led by his Star,
Be come for to worship him, e'en from afar."

When of their journey King Herod heard tell,
Himself, and all Salem, was troubled as well:
Then, calling his book-men, with ink, pen and horn,
Enquired of his clergy where Christ should be born.

Answer they made him, "As we understand,
In Bethlehem, city of Jewërie land:
For thus it is written, and plainly foretold,
By Micah the prophet in ages of old.

"O Little Bethlem, thou art not behind
The princes of Juda, the chief of their kind;
For-why out of thee shall a Monarch proceed,
The which shall my people of Israël lead."

Then callèd Herod the pilgrims to hear,
In secret, the time when the Star did appear.
And sent them to Bethlehem, saying, "Go seek,
With purpose, the Infant of whom ye do speak.

"When ye have found him, report me the news,
That I too may worship this King of the Jews."
The Magi on hearing King Herod so say,
Soon saddled and bridled and gat them away.

Then to sou'-west-ward the wonderful Star,
The which they had eyed in the East from afar,
Went ever before them until that it stay'd
Right over that house where Babe Jesus was laid.

Seeing the Star again, heart, soul and voice,
With mighty great joy did the Wise Men rejoice:
Then ent'red they in, and beheld the young Child
Together with Mary his mother so mild.

Falling with reverence low on the knee,
They worship the Infant, of highest degree:
And open their coffers; a present of myrrh,
With gold and frankincense (the gum of the fir).

Then being warnèd of God, in a dream,
Concerning King Herod, his malice and scheme,
These Easterling Sages withouten delay
Depart to their country by other-some way.

—GEORGE RATCLIFFE WOODWARD

· 114 ·

Six Green Singers

The frost of the moon fell over my floor
And six green singers stood at my door.

"What do ye here that music make?"
"Let us come in for Christ's sweet Sake."

"Long have ye journeyed in coming here?"
"Our Pilgrimage was the length of the year."

"Where do ye make for?" I asked of them.
"Our Shrine is a Stable in Bethlehem."

"What will ye do as ye go along?"
"Sing to the world an evergreen song."

"What will ye sing for the listening earth?"
"One will sing of a brave-souled Mirth,

"One of the Holiest Mystery,
The Glory of glories shall one song be,

"One of the Memory of things,
One of the Child's imaginings,

"One of our songs is the fadeless Faith,
And all are the Life more mighty than death."

"Ere ye be gone that music make,
Give me an alms for Christ's sweet Sake."

"Six green branches we leave with you;
See they be scattered your house-place through.

"This staunch blithe Holly your board shall grace,
Mistletoe bless your chimney place,

"Laurel to crown your lighted hall,
Over your bed let the Yew-bough fall,

"Close by the cradle the Christmas Fir,
For elfin dreams in its branches stir,

"Last and loveliest, high and low,
From ceil to floor let the Ivy go."

From each glad guest I received my gift
And then the latch of my door did lift—

"Green singers, God prosper the song ye make
As ye sing to the world for Christ's sweet Sake."

—ELEANOR FARJEON

Green grow'th the holly

Green grow'th the holly
So doth the ivy;
  Though winter blasts blow ne'er so high,
Green grow'th the holly.

Gay are the flowers,
Hedgerows and ploughlands;
  The days grow longer in the sun,
Soft fall the showers.

Full gold the harvest,
Grain for thy labour;
  With God must work for daily bread,
Else, man, thou starvest.

Fast fall the shed leaves,
Russet and yellow;
  But resting-buds are snug and safe
Where swung the dead leaves.

Green grow'th the holly,
So doth the ivy;
  The God of life can never die,
Hope! saith the holly.

                    (Author unknown, sixteenth century)

The Ending of the Year

When trees did show no leaves,
  And grass no daisies had,
And fields had lost their sheaves,
  And streams in ice were clad,
And day of light was shorn,
  And wind had got a spear,
Jesus Christ was born
  In the ending of the year.

Like green leaves when they grow,
   He shall for comfort be;
Like life in streams shall flow,
   For running water He;
He shall raise hope like corn
   For barren fields to bear,
And therefore He was born
   In the ending of the year.

Like daisies to the grass
   His innocence He'll bring;
In keenest winds that pass
   His flowering love shall spring;
The rising of the morn
   At midnight shall appear,
Whenever Christ is born
   In the ending of the year.

                    —ELEANOR FARJEON

Index of Titles and First Lines

Alphabetical List of Authors

Acknowledgments

Index of Titles and First Lines

Alphabetical List of Authors

Acknowledgments

The editor wishes to thank the following for their kind permission to include the following poems in this book:

"A Christmas Carol" by G. K. Chesterton, from *The Wild Knight,* by permission of E. P. Dutton & Co., Inc., New York, J. M. Dent and Sons Ltd., London, and Miss Dorothy Edith Collins.

"The Barn" by Elizabeth Coatsworth, from *Compass Rose,* by permission of Coward-McCann, Inc., New York, copyright 1929 by Coward-McCann, Inc.

"Before Dawn" by Walter de la Mare, from *Poems 1919 to 1934,* by permission of Henry Holt and Company, Inc., New York, copyright 1936 by Henry Holt and Company.

"Bethlehem-Juda, 'twas there on a morn" by George Ratcliffe Woodward, from *The Cowley Carol Book,* by permission of A. R. Mowbray & Co. Limited, London.

"By the Crib" by Katharine Tynan, by permission of The Society of Authors, London, and Miss Pamela Hinkson.

"Carol" ("High o'er the lonely hills") by Jan Struther, from *Enlarged Songs of Praise,* by permission of Oxford University Press, London.

"Carol" ("The Ox said to the Ass, said he") from *Catholic Songs* by Dorothy L. Sayers, by permission of Basil Blackwell, London.

"Carol" ("Villagers all this frosty tide") by Kenneth Grahame, from *The Wind in the Willows,* by permission of Charles Scribner's Sons, New York, copyright 1908, 1933, by Charles Scribner's Sons.

"Carol" ("When the herds were watching") by William Canton, reprinted by permission of J. M. Dent and Sons, Ltd.

"Child's Carol" by Sir Arthur Quiller-Couch, by permission of his executor, Miss Foy Quiller-Couch, Fowey, Cornwall.

"Christ Is Born" ("*Christus natus est*") by John Alexander Chapman, by permission of the author.

"Christmas at Freelands" by James Stephens, from *Collected Poems,* by permission of Mrs. Stephens and Macmillan and Company Ltd., London.

"Christmas Day" by Andrew Young, from *Collected Poems,* by permission of Jonathan Cape Limited, London.

"Christmas Eve" by John Davidson, from *Fleet Street Eclogues,* by permission of Dodd, Mead & Company, New York, and John Lane the Bodley Head Limited, London.